A WING AND A PRAYER

Jenny Dyer

'A Wing and a Prayer' was first broadcast on BBC Radio Merseyside.

Cartoons and front cover illustration by Philip Spence.

ISBN 1 85852 227 7

CONTENTS

A LONELY LADY

If you have ever prayed, and wondered if anyone heard, it may help you to know that there are offices in heaven where prayers are received and processed. Of course, you and I couldn't go there in this life, but if we could, what would we see?

We would see a vast rabbit warren of corridors and offices, staffed by angels in shirt sleeves or natty suits. We would see the prayers coming in constantly. Some come clattering in on the celestial equivalent of fax machines, some from busy people come in by e-mail, but still the most common are the prayers that come in as the heavenly equivalent of hand-written letters.

One such prayer came from Mrs J K Roberts and arrived on the desk of the archangel Gabriel. Gabriel, a tall young man with astonishingly blond hair, slipped into God's office with it. 'Letter from Mrs J K Roberts,' he said, sitting down and swinging his long legs up onto God's desk.

'Ah, yes, Mrs J K Roberts,' said God, owlish in his spectacles behind mountains of paper. 'Still using her husband's initials after all these years. Is she still so lonely?'

'I'm afraid so,' said Gabriel.

God reached for a fat file from amongst the piles on every surface of his office. It is remarkable that in an office filled with so much paper, he can unerringly lay his hands on whatever file he wants. He spread it on the table and fingered the top few letters on the pile, not as though needing to remind himself of their contents, but as though their lines were familiar to him and much loved.

'There are prayers here on every subject under heaven,' said God, patting the fat pile of letters. 'Have you told her that I love her?'

'Yes, many times,' said Gabriel. 'She knows that.'

'Tell her again,' said God. 'And we must find her some friends of flesh and blood. There's too much love in that heart of hers to waste.'

CREAM CAKES IN HEAVEN

One of the nicest things about working in heaven is that there is always an inexhaustible supply of fresh cream cakes in the fridge for those little moments of celebration.

One such happened just recently. Mabel, one of the most experienced angels in heaven, popped into God's office with some good news. Mabel exudes competence, from her sensible shoes, to her sensible skirt, to her sensible short haircut.

'Good news about Rick,' she whispered, taking a seat. God nodded. The Rick in question had recently spent a few months in prison, and in various ways had been giving Mabel considerable cause for concern.

'You remember that Rick didn't have much time for the prison chaplain,' said Mabel, 'nor indeed for religion in general? Well, something remarkable has just happened.'

Mabel paused to realise that she had an audience. A few of the younger angels had stopped in the doorway to listen. 'Rick has got himself a bed-sit, a bit of a grotty place, and last night he just couldn't stand it anymore and went for a walk along the waterfront. He was out for ages just watching the clouds, then he walked home.' Mabel paused as a few angels slipped into the office to make room for more in the doorway.

'In his room,' said Mabel, 'he just stared at the wall for a long time. Then, for the first time in his life, he prayed! "God, if you exist," he said, "you've got to help me. I'm really sorry I've made such a mess of things. I'm sick as a parrot about it all. You've got to help me start again." '

Mabel stopped and a flurry of delighted chatter broke out among the angels, falling silent as God leaned back in his chair. 'Well,' he said, 'I think this calls for a small celebration. Gabriel, the cream cakes?'

WEDDING BELLS

There is in heaven an angel called Rosvita, who has raven-black hair, huge eyes, and a figure just a little plumper than she would like. One afternoon she slipped into God's office, a little out of puff.

'Guess what?' she said, her eyes wide as saucers with excitement. 'Tell me,' said God, taking off his spectacles. An eternity of listening to prayers has not dimmed the enthusiasm with which Rosvita tells a good story, nor the pleasure with which God hears one.

'I've just heard something really, really incredible!' said Rosvita. God settled back to listen.

'Sue and Paul are getting married next month,' said Rosvita. 'Well, the vicar persuaded them to come to church, so they did for the first time today. They felt a bit awkward at first, and it felt quite strange closing their eyes for the prayers. And then in the middle of the prayers, Paul took Sue's hand and Sue smiled and hoped no-one had their eyes open and was watching them. Then,' Rosvita paused for breath – 'Then, right in the middle of the prayers, Sue thought, "While I'm here, why don't I pray for Paul and about us getting married". And Paul thought exactly the same thing! So there they were – Sue hasn't prayed since she was in school and Paul never has – and each of them was praying for the other and they really, really meant it, and the best bit is,' – Rosvita paused for effect – 'neither of them knew that the other was praying too!'

'My goodness!' said God.   Rosvita sank back in delighted triumph.

'I could just feel the blessings showering down on them! Afterwards, they just walked slowly through the churchyard and held each other's hands, feeling slightly awkward, and they said nothing about it. But do you know, I think they'll be so, so happy together.'

'Oh yes,' said God, 'I know they will.'

A WELL-NURSED GRUDGE

The archangel Gabriel is very definitely in charge up here, a tall figure sweeping through the offices, tapping on a computer keyboard here, flicking through a diary there, tossing his blond hair out of his eyes.

One morning he strode into God's office with a sheaf of freshly-arrived prayers, took a seat and swung his legs onto the desk in his usual way. God took off his spectacles and settled down to listen. 'Fax from Mr Edwards about his granddaughter,' said Gabriel. God took the fax. 'E-mail from Sarah, the chartered accountant. Says she just had to tell you you're so wonderful and she's so glad you're in her life.'

'Bless her,' smiled God, 'she has a good heart.'

'And . . . this,' said Gabriel, his forehead furrowing under the blond hair, 'from our friend above the corner shop.' Gabriel handed over the letter amounting to many sheets of dense handwritten notes. God turned the pages soberly, reading the tightly-packed lines, and between them.

'We've heard all this before,' he commented.

'I know,' said Gabriel. 'He writes all this several times a week. He's still furiously angry about it all.'

'How long ago was this alleged injustice?' asked God.

'Ten years now,' said Gabriel, 'but he keeps his anger warm, and he's using us to do it.'

God nodded. 'Does he have friends?' he asked.

'Not really anymore,' said Gabriel. 'They don't know what to do with him because he talks of nothing else.'

'He needs to find someone he can help,' said God, 'to take him out of himself. Do you think there might be any chance of him bumping into our lonely Mrs Roberts?'

'What an absolutely splendid idea,' said Gabriel, swinging his legs off the desk. 'I'll see what I can do.'

LITTLE ME

It may surprise you to know that there is an angel in heaven called Gareth. Gareth is young and tubby, for an angel, and he's still learning the ropes up here. But you're fortunate if he listens to your prayers because his heart is as big as any angel's.

Gareth gets nervous when he has to see God, especially when it is a matter of great moment, as this was. 'It's about Lynne, a mother of four kids,' he began. 'She's been very ill, but getting better now. Started praying while she was in the hospital and hasn't really stopped, though it's difficult at times, you know, to find the time.' Gareth paused.

'Go on,' said God encouragingly.

'Well, just recently, her prayers have been getting, like, really special. I thought I ought to hand her over to Gabriel 'cos I don't know what to do but he said I needed the experience.' Gareth shifted uncomfortably in his seat and God waited for him to go on.

'Well, she was praying this morning and I could tell something was going to happen, and I just held my breath, and tried to do everything I could to help her. And then I realised all the office had gone quiet and everyone up here was holding their breath for her, and just willing it to happen. And then it did! And it was such a special moment. She just suddenly thought, "Gosh, God loves me so much. Me! Little me. And God loves me this much." And that was it. It was all over in a moment. But it was so special.'

'Wonderful,' said God.

'It's the first time I've helped anyone think something that important,' said Gareth.

'Well done,' said God. 'Keep me in touch. I'm sure this is only the beginning for her.'

THE SLIPPERY SLOPE

Up here in heaven the rabbit warren of corridors and offices goes on for ever, literally, and angels flit to and fro – angels in high heels and angels in shirts and ties – collecting, processing and answering prayers as they come in. At the centre sits God, owlish behind his spectacles, in an office filled with more paper than you can imagine.

It is remarkable that God has time for every angel and every prayer that needs his attention. It was Mabel who knocked on God's open door on this particular morning. Mabel is one of God's most reliable angels, and in her flat sensible shoes, she is a model of competence and good sense.

'I'd just like to have a word with you about Rick,' she said, taking a seat by God's desk. 'I've been so happy for him. He's stayed out of trouble, got himself a better place to live, seen his ex-wife and his son a couple of times, and he even got himself a job for a few weeks. But now it's all gone wrong and he's fallen back in with his old friends.'

Mabel filled in all the details and God shook his head sadly.

'I'm very sorry for him,' said God. 'He knows what a mess he made of himself last time.'

'I think the trouble is,' said Mabel, 'that he just can't believe he can ask for forgiveness a second time. So he's going on deeper and deeper into trouble. I'm so afraid for him.'

'He will always be forgiven,' said God, 'whatever he's done, if only he'll come back.'

'Perhaps if you could try to speak to him yourself?' said Mabel. 'I just can't get through to him.'

'I will do all I can,' said God, 'if he will listen to me.'

'Thank you,' said Mabel. She smiled her sensible smile and left.

THE BEST JOB IN HEAVEN

Janice is an angel with brown curls and laughing eyes, and hers is the brightest corner of the office. That's because she has a special responsibility for listening to the prayers of children and some of her favourite prayers are pinned to the wall behind her desk. One morning Gabriel stopped by to find her busy pinning up a few new ones.

'What's that supposed to be?' he asked, indicating a scribble of green crayon on a piece of scrap paper.

'It's a puppy,' said Janice. 'Thomas' mum is expecting a baby and Thomas has asked God to make it a puppy.'

'Ah,' said Gabriel, 'and how about this spotty one?'

'That's Ben's friend,' said Janice. 'Ben wants God to give him chicken pox.'

'How charming!' said Gabriel. 'Are any of these serious prayers?'

'Oh, they're all serious,' said Janice, turning her laughing eyes on Gabriel.

'No, I mean can any of them be answered?' asked Gabriel.

'They all get answered,' said Janice, 'one way or another. God finds a way to answer the need behind the request.'

Gabriel surveyed the pieces of paper on the wall: the carefully coloured drawings of ten year olds, the squiggles of toddlers, the higgledy-piggledy writing – 'Please help Mummy to get better.' 'Please feed all the hungry children.' 'Please make it nice weather at half-term.' 'Please bring my friend Laura's Daddy back.' Janice followed his gaze.

'So I take it you don't feel like moving on to something a little more grown up?' asked Gabriel with a smile.

'Children are so honest when they pray,' said Janice. 'They're never afraid of saying what's really on their mind. I have the best job in heaven.'

NOTHING

The archangel Gabriel, a young man with long legs and astonishingly blond hair, was standing by the fax machine, his brow furrowed. The fax machine was disconcertingly silent, and so was Gabriel, and so was the office. Angels tip-toed about their business, spoke in hushed voices, opened and closed files quietly.

Gabriel was waiting for a prayer from a particular individual. He had been waiting several days. The angel Rosvita came up and slipped an arm round Gabriel's waist. Even in her high heels she was nowhere near tall enough to put an arm round his shoulders.

'Nothing yet?' she asked kindly.

'Nothing,' said Gabriel without taking his eyes off the fax machine.

'Don't worry, it'll come,' said Rosvita.

'He was so much on fire,' said Gabriel. 'He prayed every day, sometimes for an hour or more. He was so much alive. Then one morning he woke up and thought, "What if it's all a mistake? What if there is no God?" 'Now . . .' Gabriel shrugged, 'nothing.'

'Oh dear, it happens so easily!' said Rosvita.

'It's real despair,' said Gabriel. 'He's plunged into blackness. It's awful.'

'Come away,' said Rosvita. 'We'll let you know as soon as anything comes in.'

Suddenly the fax machine rang, and clattered uncertainly into life. It printed out one line. Gabriel tore off the piece of paper and read, ' "O God, help me!" '

'There you are,' said Rosvita, 'he's taken the first step. He'll get there. Come away now.'

Gabriel had a tear in his eye, and his tread was heavy, but at least now he turned away, folding the paper and slipping it into a pocket.

GOD BLESS MY BABY

God looked up from his paperwork as pretty plump Rosvita, with the raven-black hair and huge eyes, bounced into his office.

'Good news again, Rosvita?' he asked. Good news follows Rosvita around.

'I just have to tell you about Sue and Paul,' she said. 'They took their baby for the christening on Sunday, and it was so lovely! The baby is so beautiful! Do you remember that Sue and Paul said their very first prayer in that church just a few weeks before they got married?'

'I do,' said God, 'and were they praying at the christening?'

'No!' said Rosvita, 'They were much too nervous. But lots of other people were praying. Look!' She produced a sheaf of prayers. 'It's so lovely!' said Rosvita, 'All those people praying for one tiny baby at the same time. Look, this one's from the baby's Nana. And this one's from the organist. He's a great saint and says the most lovely prayers.'

God leafed through the papers. 'So, none from Sue and Paul?' he asked, with a glint in his eyes.

'Ah, that's the best bit,' said Rosvita, her eyes as big as saucers. She took out of her file a few small pieces of paper, flattened them and handed them to God one at a time. 'This one was from Sue a couple of weeks before the christening,' she said. 'And just a few days before. And this one was Paul just the night before. And these were Sue and these were Paul since then.'

God studied the shy little phrases. 'God bless my baby.' 'Please God, make it a good world for my child to grow up in.' 'Please God, look after our baby and make us good enough to be her parents.' 'Help us to love her enough.' 'Help us to deserve her.'

'Well done, Rosvita,' said God. 'You've done really well in helping these people to pray.'

'Oh, I've done nothing,' said Rosvita. 'It's that gorgeous baby.'

HOSPITAL REPORT

The tubby young angel, Gareth, is now working in the hospital department in heaven with a much more experienced angel called Joyce. You can imagine that many, many prayers come in from hospitals and Joyce, Gareth and their colleagues are kept very busy.

One evening as everyone else was going home they collected their files together and went to make their report to God. Gareth set the pile of files on the floor and Joyce took a seat.

'You've had a busy day,' said God.

'Very busy,' said Joyce, taking off her half-rimmed glasses and rubbing her eyes. 'The hospital is full, and quite a number of operations have been cancelled.'

One by one, Gareth passed God the files and Joyce talked about the people, and the prayers that had been prayed, and Gareth nervously put in an odd word. Slowly, meticulously, they talked through every prayer that had been prayed that day.

'Then there's Frank on ward B9 . . .' said Joyce. Gareth spread the file open on God's desk and God, who knew the details as well as Frank's own family, smoothed the pages and sighed.

It was remarkable, thought Gareth, how God could go on listening to prayer after prayer, day after day, eternity after eternity. God's concentration never faltered, and his infinite kindness never dimmed. Together they struggled with what should be done, and Gareth jotted down a list of action points on a clipboard. One for every prayer. In some way or another, every prayer was answered.

'That's everyone,' said Joyce finally, sitting back in her chair. God leaned back too, a small figure with all the sorrows of the world on his shoulders, but with lively eyes, full of love. 'Well done, you've worked hard,' he said. Gareth gathered up the files and they left, passing another pair of angels on their way in. Another hospital, another day, another report.

A SQUADDY AND HIS AUNT

Those people who pray every day for the same person are well-known in heaven. Every angel knows their name. Every angel looks on them as a colleague. They are part of heaven's workforce. One such is Mrs B Harris, who prays every day for her nephew, Joseph, who is in the army overseas.

The angel Timothy, an efficient and businesslike soul, has charge of Mrs Harris' file and he has just been in God's office making his daily report.

'How is our good friend, Mrs Harris?' asked God, cleaning his spectacles as Timothy prepared to leave.

'She's well,' said Timothy. 'Her nephew Joe has had one or two brushes with his superiors. He's fond of a drink and he can be a bit wild, but basically he's settling down. The really loutish behaviour is, I think, now well in the past.'

'Good,' said God. 'And she still prays for him every day?'

'Every day,' said Timothy, 'for his health, his safety, his relationship with his girlfriend, his career, his future in every way. It's always a delight to hear from her.'

'And does Joe ever pray?' asked God.

'He has done, a few times,' said Tim, 'once or twice when he has got into a sticky situation, once for a friend after an accident, that sort of thing. It embarrasses him to know that his aunt prays for him but, when his back's to the wall, he thinks of her. I think he will be a good man. I think in the end her example and her prayers will have done him more good than either of them will ever realise.'

'Good,' said God, 'let her know again how much we appreciate her. We need her, and as many more like her as we can get.'

A BLACK FILE

The archangel Gabriel found the angel Edna sighing over a file on her desk. The file was fat and full. What's worse, it was black. In heaven, black is the colour for prayers prayed in bitterness, spite, hatred and vindictiveness.

'Whose file is that?' asked Gabriel.

'It's Alan's,' said Edna. 'His marriage is collapsing. Well, it has really collapsed, and he's finding it very difficult.'

'That would appear to be an understatement,' said Gabriel, lifting the file and feeling its weight, and the weight of misery contained therein.

'The circumstances are unusually cruel,' said Edna. 'And they had been so much in love for so long. It is very hard. Love and fury are I think two sides of one coin.'

Edna has grey hair and grey eyes, a lined and worried brow and, always, a string of pearls. Her eternity has been full of cares, but always cares for other people; and she cares with kindness and gentleness.

'What is he praying for?' asked Gabriel.

'He prays as an excuse to rehearse yet again how he feels,' said Edna. 'He is practising the pain. He is almost beginning to enjoy the pain. He is becoming the pain. It's that that frightens me. I'm trying to help him move on. I'm waiting for the day when he can pray *for* his wife, and ask forgiveness for the things *he* has thought and said in all this, some of which have been terrible.'

'Is he getting there?' asked Gabriel.

'It will be a long time,' said Edna, 'but,' and she slipped an empty yellow file out from under the fat black one, 'I already have a yellow file with his name on, ready for that day.'

THE WALL MAP

On Thursdays, the angel Gareth does a shift on the wall map. The map fills the whole of one wall of a large office. It shows the world, with areas of special concern marked up and colour coded. It is the job of the angel on duty to climb up and down a wheeled ladder all day, updating the map and pinning on it prayers as they come in from round the world.

Penny appeared at the foot of the ladder, almost hidden behind a huge pile of paper in her arms.

'Gareth, more prayers for you,' she called.

Gareth clambered down the ladder, slightly pink from the exercise. 'Lots from West Africa because of the situation,' said Penny, 'and Alice and Bernard's special delivery for today has just arrived.'

Alice and Bernard are excellently well-informed people who pray together every day for needs all round the world. Their prayers are full of what they have read in the newspapers, and of deep Christian concern. They are much respected in heaven, and their fulsome prayers each day are awaited with some eagerness.

Penny left Gareth sorting the papers, climbing up and down the ladder to fix them up, and slicing Alice and Bernard's missive into strips, so as to pin the prayers to the relevant parts of the world. When he has finished his shift, the map will be all but obliterated by a great mass of prayer.

This map is more than a wall-chart. That's what it may look like, but it is in fact a power-house. This is the engine-room of God's justice and mercy for a world in trouble.

HEAVENLY MUSIC

The archangel Gabriel stood up at his desk, pushed his blond hair out of his eyes, gathered up a sheaf of particularly perplexing prayers on which he needed God's input, and headed for God's office. He was at the door and had nearly turned the knob, when it dawned on him that the door was not usually closed. Glancing through the pane of glass, he saw God, his spectacles off, his eyes shut, and a blissful expression on his face.

Gabriel understood. God was listening. He was listening to earth, to some of the prayers there that he found most beautiful. Gabriel did not know what it was this time, but perhaps it was the choir of some great cathedral, worship soaring to the high vaulted roof. Or perhaps it was the pious repetition in some quiet place of ancient well-loved prayers, perhaps in a monastery chapel or a country church. Or perhaps it was wordless but wonder-filled contemplation of a soul long experienced in the ways of prayer. Some prayers can be heard only in heaven.

Gabriel hesitated with his hand on the doorknob. He looked again at God's expression. Then he flicked through the prayers he had brought for discussion. The prayers of the disturbed, the frightened, the despairing, the insane. All of them were urgent and God would want to know about them. All of them needed answering. But then again, perhaps all of them could wait a little while, given that a little while in heaven is nothing at all on earth. Gabriel turned and stole quietly back to his desk, leaving God to enjoy for a few minutes the devotion of his people.

CHOCOLATES

The archangel Gabriel was disturbed at his work by the chattering of a noisy flock of angels round Joyce's desk, in the hospital department. Striding up, and having the advantage of being tall enough to look over the other angels, Gabriel saw an open box of chocolates on Joyce's desk and everyone excitedly helping themselves.

'A celebration!' he said, squeezing through the crowd, which parted respectfully for him. He selected a chocolate for himself. 'Does this mean that someone has remembered to say thank you for an answered prayer?'

'Yes indeed,' said Joyce, smiling under her half-rimmed spectacles like a cat that's got the cream. She produced a letter with a flourish and handed it to Gabriel.

Gabriel perused the neat handwriting, a shy and formal prayer of thanks offered in a hospital chapel. The writer and her husband had evidently been praying a great deal for their daughter, who had been seriously ill but who was now well on the way to recovery.

'Congratulations,' said Gabriel, handing back the letter and helping himself to another chocolate. 'You must be very proud.'

'I am,' said Joyce, putting the lid firmly on the chocolate box to preserve the last three chocolates for herself. 'Many prayers have been answered here in many wonderful ways, but it's a little while since anyone said thank you. And when they do,' she said with mock severity to the other angels, 'everyone eats my chocolates.'

'Back to work, then,' said Gabriel, and the flurry of angels returned to their desks and their work.

It doesn't often happen that people remember to say thank you when prayers are answered, but if they do, there are chocolates for everyone in heaven.